G000160871

For my
BEST FRIEND
FOREVER

giggles

hugs

Purple Ronnie

summersdale

FOR MY BEST FRIEND FOREVER

Summersdale Publishers Ltd
46 West Street
Chichester
West Sussex
PO19 1RP
UK

www.summersdale.com

www.purpleronnie.com

Printed and bound in the Czech Republic

ISBN: 978-1-84953-878-7

Substantial discounts on bulk quantities of Summersdale books are available to corporations, professional associations and other organisations. For details contact general enquiries: telephone: +44 (0) 1243 771107, fax: +44 (0) 1243 786300 or email: enquiries@summersdale.com.

To.....................................

From...............................

You always know
what I'm thinking
It's like our brains
are synced
You read my mind
with just a look
Cos of our freaky
best-friend link!

You're my
ultimate fave!

Amount of mischief I can get up to on my own...

... Amount of mischief I can get up to with you

I like our giggly sleepovers
With fashion shows and cake
And midnight feasts
for breakfast
Cos we couldn't
stay awake!

I think I've pinched
half your books
And two thirds of your DVDs
But as they say, fair is fair
Cos you've borrowed all
mine from me!

Let's have a day of being silly and free

The ultimate BFF kit:

Ancient BFF necklaces

That jumper that either belongs to you or me (we can't remember)

Phone bill
from all
the data
we've used
chatting to
each other

A wall of
all our
photos and
memories

Let's go climb a mountain
Or ride a bike for two
Whatever the adventure
It's best when I'm with you!

You always
know just how to
cheer me up!

How long it seems like
we spend on the phone...

... How long we ACTUALLY spend on the phone

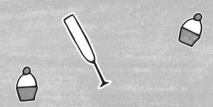

You're wonderful
you're super
You really are top notch
Let's celebrate
our friendship
By going somewhere posh!

I can trust you
with any secret —
no matter how big!

What we think we look like when we spend time together...

... What we actually look like when we spend time together

Life isn't always amazing
Sometimes it seems
a bit pants
But you help me shake off
the bad days
With some gossip and
plenty of bants!

I think my thumbs
have worn away
from all the
messaging we do!

You're such a legend, bestie
You have a heart of gold
I think that when
they made you
They broke the bestie mould

I've uploaded all our selfies
Posted status updates too
Because I want to
tell the world
That I'm best friends
with you!

If there were medals for best friends, you'd get gold!

A normal weekend's plans

checklist without you

- wash hair

- clean room

- do recycling

- find lost things

- watch rubbish TV

checklist with you

-rocket ship for
 trip to Moon

-five hours non-
 stop laughing

-snacks — all very
 unhealthy

A BFF weekend's plans

You can keep me laughing
For an hour straight, or three
Until I have to shout 'Stop!'
Cos I think I'm going to wee!

#bff
#forreal

A three-legged
race with one...

... A three-legged
race with two

I know that I'm not
ultra-perfect
My outfits aren't always
too sleek
But you wouldn't care
if I had no hair
Or dressed like the
nerdiest geek

You inspire me
to be the best I
can be! #sweats

A normal takeaway pizza...

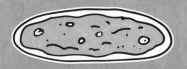

... A takeaway pizza
shared with you

You're beautiful
inside and out
And gorgeous in every way
Whether you're in an LBD
Or it's a slippers
and PJs day!

OMG our friendship
is trending

... It's lucky WE'RE
both perfect

You've split dessert and
helped me move
You're there if I'm in need
So give me a shout if you
need helping out
Cos you're a special
friend indeed!

You're a treasure

Thank you for laughing at my jokes... even when they're lame

When you're feeling peckish
And I've got some
choc to spare
I'll gladly hand it over
(But please save me
a square)

We love a
good drama

Shopping on my own...

... Shopping with you

Salad and keep-fit classes
Can make you feel
healthy it's true
But I'd much rather
go into town
For movies and popcorn
with you

Thank you for
organising all those
great days out –
and the nights too!

How to deal with heartbreak:

Cry into your pillow

Ask your BFF to
come round

If there's lippy
on my teeth
Or a button's come undone
You'll always save
my blushes
Cos you're bestie
number one

You have the BEST
taste in everything...

... especially friends!

A problem shared is a problem halved!

The early-morning grump

The early-morning
grump plus friends

Let's grow old together
We'll have a grey old time,

We'll look like sweet
old ladies
But really be
partners in crime!

You are my
life guru

I'd love to win the lottery
A million would be nice,
But I couldn't buy
our friendship
Cos it comes without
a price!

Some people try very hard
To show how cool they are
You don't need to try at all
You were born a superstar!

Whether we haven't spoken for a week or we haven't STOPPED speaking for a week, I've always got loads to say to you

Sometimes I get
a bit grumpy
Other times you're
feeling glum
But together we just
can't help smiling
That's why you're my
favourite chum!